Also by Bill Watterson:

CALVIN AND HOBBES
SOMETHING UNDER THE BED IS DROOLING
YUKON HO!
WEIRDOS FROM ANOTHER PLANET
LAZY SUNDAY BOOK
REVENGE OF THE BABY-SAT
THE AUTHORITATIVE CALVIN AND HOBBES
SCIENTIFIC PROGRESS GOES 'BOINK'
ATTACK OF THE DERANGED MUTANT KILLER MONSTER SNOW GOONS

Taken from CALVIN AND HOBBES:
CALVIN AND HOBBES 1: THEREBY HANGS A TALE
CALVIN AND HOBBES 2: ONE DAY THE WIND WILL CHANGE

Calvin and Hobbes

3: IN THE SHADOW OF THE NIGHT

BILL WATTERSON

A *Warner* Book

First published in Great Britain in 1992
by Warner Books

ISBN 0 7474 1160 3

Printed and bound in Great Britain by
Cox & Wyman Ltd, Reading

Warner Books
A Division of
Little, Brown and Company (UK) Limited
165 Great Dover Street
London SE1 4YA

TO MELISSA

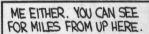

THE RAIN STOPPED!

THIS IS THE BEST TIME TO GO WORMMUCKING. LET'S GO!

WHAT'S THAT?

IT'S WHEN YOU WALK ON THE PAVEMENT AND MUCK ALL THE WORMS.

HURRY UP, CALVIN. OUR RESERVATION IS FOR 7:00.

CAN HOBBES COME TO THE RESTAURANT?

NO.

WHY NOT?

WE'RE AFRAID HE MIGHT EAT SOMEONE. LET'S GO.

THAT'S RIGHT. YOU PROBABLY *WOULD*, WOULDN'T YOU?

I CAN NEVER STAY ON A DIET IN A RESTAURANT.

EVERYBODY I KNOW HAS EITHER CABLE TV OR A VCR! THEY CAN WATCH ANYTHING THEY WANT!

BUT ME? *I* HAVE TO WATCH DUMB OL' SUMMER REPEATS! *I* HAVE TO WATCH THE SAME GARBAGE OVER AND OVER!

HOW CRUELLY WE MISTREAT YOU, CALVIN.

...SO THEN HE GAVE ME "OLIVER TWIST" TO READ, AND SAID I MIGHT IDENTIFY WITH IT.

RATS... AND "SORORITY ROW HORROR" IS ON CABLE TONIGHT.

FLUSH!

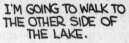

FLOWERS ARE PRETTY STUPID.

SEE, IT'S A BRIGHT, SUNNY DAY OUT, RIGHT?

WELL, WITH THIS WATERING CAN, I CAN MAKE THEM THINK IT'S RAINING.

IT'S FUN TO MESS WITH THEIR MINDS.

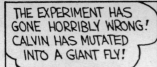

THE EXPERIMENT HAS GONE HORRIBLY WRONG! CALVIN HAS MUTATED INTO A GIANT FLY!

HE ZIPS ABOUT IN PARASITIC HUNGER, SEARCHING FOR DECAYING FLESH!

AN UNBEARABLE STENCH FILLS THE AIR. THE HIDEOUS BUG ZEROES IN.

MMM! THIS MAKES ME HUNGRY!

DON'T BE GROSS. JUST TAKE OUT THE GARBAGE LIKE I ASKED YOU, WILL YOU PLEASE?

WATTERSON

IT'S ANOTHER NEW MORNING FOR MR. MONROE. HE GLANCES AT THE NEWSPAPER HEADLINES OVER A CUP OF COFFEE, AND GETS IN HIS RED SPORTS CAR TO GO TO WORK.

LITTLE DOES HE REALIZE IT'S HIS LAST DAY ON THE FACE OF THE EARTH!

CALVIN DRINKS THE MAGIC ELIXIR AND BEGINS AN INCREDIBLE TRANSFORMATION!

INSTANTLY HE GROWS! BIGGER AND BIGGER! HIGHER AND HIGHER!

I CAN'T BELIEVE MY MOM SIGNED ME UP FOR SWIMMING LESSONS.

HERE I AM FREEZING MY BUNS OFF AT 9 IN THE MORNING, ABOUT TO JUMP INTO ICE WATER AND DROWN.

THE ONLY THING THAT COULD POSSIBLY MAKE THIS WORSE WOULD BE IF THE CLASS WAS...

...TAUGHT BY MY SADISTIC BABY SITTER!!

WELL, LOOK WHO'S HERE!

FLYING LOW OVER THE GRASS, HE SEARCHES FOR DEAD MEAT!

UP AND OVER THE FLOWERS, DARTING THIS WAY AND THAT!

OH NO! HE'S CAUGHT IN A SPIDER WEB!

THRASHING ABOUT IN A DESPERATE BID FOR FREEDOM, HE ONLY BECOMES MORE ENTANGLED! SOON THE SPIDER WILL SUCK OUT HIS INNARDS! HELP!

I WAS GOING TO JOIN YOU IN THE HAMMOCK, BUT I THINK I'LL FORGET IT.

WHACK!

TELL ME THIS ISN'T A SPITBALL!!

..RRRRRRR...

A WATER BALLOON! THAT DIRTY TIGER ESCALATED THE WAR! THIS CALLS FOR SUPREME RETALIATION!

I'LL GET HIM WITH THE GARDEN HOSE! NOTHING CAN BEAT A HOSE FOR SHEER VOLUME OF WATER!

...UNLESS, OF COURSE, HE WENT SO FAR AS TO...

WATERSON

YOU KNOW, DAD, IT DISTURBS ME THAT THIS WAGON HAS NO SEAT BELTS AND WOULDN'T SURVIVE A 30 MPH IMPACT WITH A STATIONARY OBJECT.

UM... WHY DO YOU BRING THIS UP?

OH, NO REASON.

WANT TO HELP ME TEST THE THEORY OF RELATIVITY?

SURE.

THE IDEA IS THAT THE FASTER WE GO, THE SLOWER TIME GOES.

GOTCHA. IT'S 10:23.

WHAT'S ALL THE RUCKUS?! YOU'RE SUPPOSED TO BE ASLEEP!

AND WHAT'S WITH ALL THESE FEATHERS?! ARE YOU TEARING UP YOUR PILLOWS?!

IT WAS INCREDIBLE, DAD! A HERD OF DUCKS FLEW IN THE WINDOW AND MOLTED! THEY LEFT WHEN THEY HEARD YOU COMING! HONEST!

NICE ALIBI, FRIZZLETOP! NO DESSERT FOR A WEEK!

YOU WANT ANOTHER PILLOW ACROSS THE KISSER? I DIDN'T HEAR *YOU* OFFER ANY BRAINSTORMS!

YOU SEE, HOBBES, *I* HAVE A WATER BALLOON, AND *YOU* DON'T.

I THEREFORE HAVE OFFENSIVE SUPERIORITY, SO YOU HAVE TO DO WHAT I SAY. WHAT DO YOU THINK OF THAT?

I THINK I'LL TAKE THIS STICK AND POKE YOUR BALLOON.

THAT'S THE TROUBLE WITH WEAPONS TECHNOLOGY. IT BECOMES OBSOLETE SO QUICKLY.

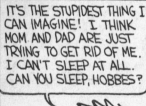

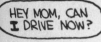

Warner Books now offers an exciting range of quality titles by both established and new authors. All of the books in this series are available from:
Little, Brown and Company (UK) Limited,
Cash Sales Department,
P.O. Box 11,
Falmouth,
Cornwall TR10 9EN.

Alternatively you may fax your order to the above address. Fax No. 0326 376423.

Payments can be made as follows: cheque, postal order (payable to Little, Brown and Company) or by credit cards, Visa/Access. Do not send cash or currency. UK customers and B.F.P.O. please allow £1.00 for postage and packing for the first book, plus 50p for the second book, plus 30p for each additional book up to a maximum charge of £3.00 (7 books plus).

Overseas customers including Ireland, please allow £2.00 for postage and packing for the first book plus £1.00 for the second book, plus 50p for each additional book.

NAME (Block Letters) ....

....

ADDRESS ....

....

....

☐ I enclose my remittance for _____

☐ I wish to pay by Access/Visa Card

Number ⬚⬚⬚⬚⬚⬚⬚⬚⬚⬚⬚⬚⬚⬚⬚⬚⬚

Card Expiry Date ⬚⬚⬚⬚